the ultimate
SKETCH
JOURNAL
FOR JEWELRY ARTISTS

RENA TUCKER

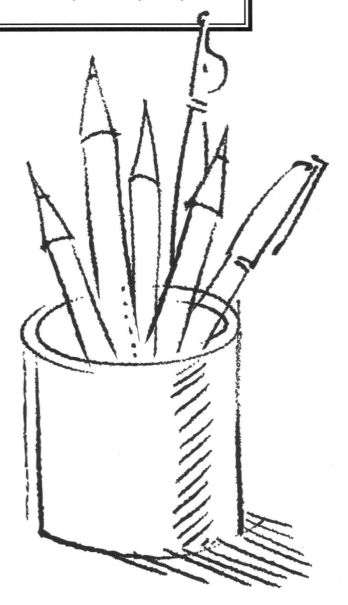

Published by Journal A Month Publications
an imprint of Rampart Publishing

Copyright © 2016 Rena Tucker

www.JournalsRock.com

Cover image by J. L. Pfeifer
Pencils + Pens illustration by Alena Hovorkova

ISBN 978-1-946305-03-9

TO ALL THE JEWELRY ARTISTS.

WITHOUT YOU, OUR EARS, NECKS, WRISTS,
AND FINGERS WOULD GO UNADORNED…

WHICH WOULD MAKE GETTING DRESSED
UNSPEAKABLY BORING.

CONTENTS

ABOUT THE ULTIMATE SKETCH JOURNAL FOR JEWELRY ARTISTS

OVERVIEW

Artists have used sketchbooks as a primary creative tool for centuries. Both non-artists and artists alike have kept journals to explore and record their ideas, emotions, observations, questions, internal and external processes, challenges, discoveries, and victories.

The Ultimate Sketch Journal for Jewelry Artists is a creative tool that fuses journaling, planning + sketching. It's an efficient and attactive way to keep the details of your jewelry making projects in one place, plus it will help you refine your signature style and unique approach to making jewelry.

GOAL

The Ultimate Sketch Journal for Jewelry Artists is designed to support every aspect of your creative process as you work through 30 jewelry projects of any type or size, all the way from ideation and planning through creation/fabrication, and ultimately making a record of your finished pieces.

Whether it takes you 30, 60, 90, 180 days, or even longer, you'll be amazed and proud to look back on all you've accomplished after completing your 30 projects and filling up the pages of your Sketch Journal!

FORMAT

The Ultimate Sketch Journal for Jewelry Artists contains a total of 30 sections, one for each project.

You'll be recording everything from the physical/technical aspects (type of jewelry items, dimensions, style, materials, etc.) to your mental process (ideas, observations, problem solving) to the final details (suggested wearing/pairing items, and sale or gifting info.)

Organizing information in this manner results in a gorgeous, complete history of all your projects, and it makes it easy to identify and purchase more of the same materials.

10 TIPS FOR USING THIS SKETCH JOURNAL

#01 — <u>IMPORTANT</u>!!! The paper in this Sketch Journal is NOT designed to accept water, oil, or solvent-based media. Feel free to *go nutty* with pencil, colored pencil, charcoal, ballpoint pen or "no-bleed" pens, but if you want to use watercolors or markers, be sure to test them on a small area first, or just use loose paper. (Adding loose sheets of paper is fun!)

#02 — KEEP IT HANDY. Keeping your Sketch Journal nearby lets you capture your process in real time. It's easy to forget important details if you wait until you're done.

#03 — FILL IN THE BLANKS on the Contents page with descriptive names of your projects. This makes it super easy to go back and find information when you need it.

#04 — KNOW WHEN TO STOP. Goals + Intentions are the things you want to accomplish, such as: Trying a new material or technique, creating a piece for sale, etc.

#05 — MATERIALS LIST = BLISS. Notes on products and hardware are *pure gold*. With infinite combinations of beads, gemstones, wire, chain, findings, doodads, etc., the best way to keep track of it all is to write down what you use, number it, then write the corresponding numbers on the sketch/pattern where you used them in your project. Or, draw lines + arrows. Don't worry about neatness—you're creating a reference for *yourself*.

#06 — WRITE REVIEWS. Recording your impressions of products and brands in terms of quality, ease of use, etc. will save you time, money, and frustration in the future.

#07 — EMBRACE YOUR GENIUS. Challenges + Solutions and **Discoveries + Lessons Learned** are prompts for internalizing your "aha" moments. Be sure to capture them as they happen, then review and add to them after you finish a project.

#08 — CELEBRATE & LET GO. What I'd change/do differently and **What I like about my project** are prompts for experiencing completion and a sense of wholeness, both of which are essential for growth and momentum.

#09 — BUILD A STASH. The **Things to try** prompt teases out a "stash" of ideas for whenever you need blast of inspiration or want to challenge yourself.

#10 — DON'T SKIP THE WRAP UP. The **Finished Project Info** and **Photo(s)** sections help you document sale/gifting info for both "follow up" and income tax purposes.

x

I always accessorize with jewelry…
I love sparkles, and so wearing jewelry
makes me feel more exciting,
and confident, too!

AMBER LE BON

PROJECT 01

Type of Project/**Description**: _____

_____

Inspiration: _____

_____

Goals + **Intentions**: _____

_____

_____

_____

Style + **Color Scheme**: _____

Dimensions: _____

Date **Started**: _____ Date **Finished**: _____

Beads, **Gemstones** + **Other Products** Used: _____

_____

_____

_____

_____

Wire, Findings, Chain + **Other Hardware**: _____

_____

_____

_____

_____

Techniques + Methods: _____

_____

_____

_____

_____

REFERENCE PHOTO(S) / INSTRUCTIONS

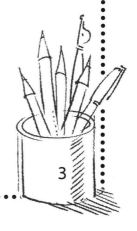

PROJECT SKETCH / PATTERN

4

FINISHED PROJECT PHOTO(S)

PROJECT 02

Type of Project/**Description**: _____

_____

Inspiration: _____

_____

Goals + **Intentions**: _____

_____

_____

_____

Style + **Color Scheme**: _____

Dimensions: _____

Date **Started**: _____ Date **Finished**: _____

Beads, Gemstones + **Other Products** Used: _____

_____

_____

_____

_____

Wire, Findings, Chain + **Other Hardware**: _____

_____

_____

_____

_____

Techniques + Methods: _____

_____

_____

_____

_____

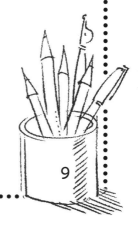

9

PROJECT SKETCH / PATTERN

THOUGHTS & INSIGHTS

Challenges + **solutions**: _____

_____

_____

_____

_____

_____

Discoveries + lessons learned: _____

_____

_____

_____

_____

_____

_____

What I would **change** or **do differently**: _____

_____

_____

_____

_____

_____

What I **like about my project**: _____

_____

_____

_____

_____

_____

Things to try in the future: _____

_____

_____

_____

_____

_____

FINISHED PROJECT INFO

Suggested or **included** wearing/pairing items: _____

_____

_____

_____

_____

_____

_____

Kept, **gifted**, or **offered for sale**? _____

Price or **other valuation**: _____

If gifted or sold, **recipient/buyer** details: _____

_____

_____

_____

_____

_____

_____

_____

Other: _____

_____

_____

_____

_____

_____

_____

_____

_____

_____

FINISHED PROJECT PHOTO(S)

PROJECT 03

Type of Project/**Description**: _____

_____

Inspiration: _____

_____

Goals + **Intentions**: _____

_____

_____

_____

Style + **Color Scheme**: _____

Dimensions: _____

Date **Started**: _____ Date **Finished**: _____

Beads, Gemstones + **Other Products** Used: _____

_____

_____

_____

_____

Wire, Findings, Chain + **Other Hardware**: _____

_____

_____

_____

_____

Techniques + Methods: _____

_____

_____

_____

_____

REFERENCE PHOTO(S) / INSTRUCTIONS

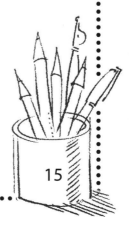

15

THOUGHTS & INSIGHTS

Challenges + **solutions**: _____

_____

_____

_____

_____

_____

Discoveries + lessons learned: _____

_____

_____

_____

_____

_____

What I would **change** or **do differently**: _____

_____

_____

_____

_____

_____

What I **like about my project**: _____

_____

_____

_____

_____

_____

Things to try in the future: _____

_____

_____

_____

_____

_____

FINISHED PROJECT INFO

Suggested or **included** wearing/pairing items: _____

_____

_____

_____

_____

_____

_____

Kept, **gifted**, or **offered for sale**? _____

Price or **other valuation**: _____

If gifted or sold, **recipient**/**buyer** details: _____

_____

_____

_____

_____

_____

_____

_____

Other: _____

_____

_____

_____

_____

_____

_____

_____

_____

_____

_____

FINISHED PROJECT PHOTO(S)

PROJECT 04

Type of Project/**Description**: _____

_____

Inspiration: _____

_____

Goals + **Intentions**: _____

_____

_____

_____

Style + **Color Scheme**: _____

Dimensions: _____

Date **Started**: _____ Date **Finished**: _____

Beads, **Gemstones** + **Other Products** Used: _____

_____

_____

_____

_____

Wire, Findings, Chain + **Other Hardware**: _____

_____

_____

_____

_____

Techniques + Methods: _____

_____

_____

_____

_____

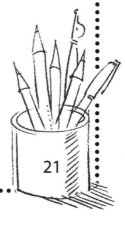

22

THOUGHTS & INSIGHTS

Challenges + **solutions**: _____

_____

_____

_____

_____

_____

Discoveries + lessons learned: _____

_____

_____

_____

_____

_____

What I would **change** or **do differently**: _____

_____

_____

_____

_____

_____

What I **like about my project**: _____

_____

_____

_____

_____

_____

Things to try in the future: _____

_____

_____

_____

_____

_____

FINISHED PROJECT INFO

Suggested or **included** wearing/pairing items: _____

_____

_____

_____

_____

_____

_____

Kept, **gifted**, or **offered for sale**? _____

Price or **other valuation**: _____

If gifted or sold, **recipient/buyer** details: _____

_____

_____

_____

_____

_____

_____

_____

Other: _____

_____

_____

_____

_____

_____

_____

_____

_____

_____

_____

FINISHED PROJECT PHOTO(S)

PROJECT 05

Type of Project/**Description**: _____

_____

Inspiration: _____

_____

Goals + **Intentions**: _____

_____

_____

_____

Style + **Color Scheme**: _____

Dimensions: _____

Date **Started**: _____ Date **Finished**: _____

Beads, Gemstones + **Other Products** Used: _____

_____

_____

_____

_____

Wire, Findings, Chain + **Other Hardware**: _____

_____

_____

_____

_____

Techniques + Methods: _____

_____

_____

_____

_____

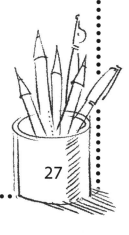

27

28

THOUGHTS & INSIGHTS

Challenges + **solutions**: _____

_____

_____

_____

_____

_____

Discoveries + lessons learned: _____

_____

_____

_____

_____

_____

What I would **change** or **do differently**: _____

_____

_____

_____

_____

_____

What I **like about my project**: _____

_____

_____

_____

_____

_____

Things to try in the future: _____

_____

_____

_____

_____

_____

FINISHED PROJECT INFO

Suggested or **included** wearing/pairing items: _____

_____

_____

_____

_____

_____

_____

Kept, **gifted**, or **offered for sale**? _____

Price or **other valuation**: _____

If gifted or sold, **recipient**/**buyer** details: _____

_____

_____

_____

_____

_____

_____

_____

Other: _____

_____

_____

_____

_____

_____

_____

_____

_____

_____

_____

FINISHED PROJECT PHOTO(S)

PROJECT 06

Type of Project/**Description**: _____

_____

Inspiration: _____

_____

Goals + **Intentions**: _____

_____

_____

_____

Style + **Color Scheme**: _____

Dimensions: _____

Date **Started**: _____ Date **Finished**: _____

Beads, Gemstones + **Other Products** Used: _____

_____

_____

_____

_____

Wire, Findings, Chain + **Other Hardware**: _____

_____

_____

_____

_____

Techniques + Methods: _____

_____

_____

_____

_____

REFERENCE PHOTO(S) / INSTRUCTIONS

33

PROJECT SKETCH / PATTERN

34

THOUGHTS & INSIGHTS

Challenges + **solutions**: _____

_____

_____

_____

_____

_____

Discoveries + lessons learned: _____

_____

_____

_____

_____

_____

What I would **change** or **do differently**: _____

_____

_____

_____

_____

_____

What I **like about my project**: _____

_____

_____

_____

_____

_____

Things to try in the future: _____

_____

_____

_____

_____

_____

FINISHED PROJECT INFO

Suggested or **included** wearing/pairing items: _____

_____

_____

_____

_____

_____

_____

Kept, **gifted**, or **offered for sale**? _____

Price or **other valuation**: _____

If gifted or sold, **recipient**/**buyer** details: _____

_____

_____

_____

_____

_____

_____

_____

Other: _____

_____

_____

_____

_____

_____

_____

_____

_____

_____

FINISHED PROJECT PHOTO(S)

PROJECT 07

Type of Project/**Description**: _____

_____

Inspiration: _____

_____

Goals + **Intentions**: _____

_____

_____

_____

Style + **Color Scheme**: _____

Dimensions: _____

Date **Started**: _____ Date **Finished**: _____

Beads, Gemstones + **Other Products** Used: _____

_____

_____

_____

_____

Wire, Findings, Chain + **Other Hardware**: _____

_____

_____

_____

_____

Techniques + Methods: _____

_____

_____

_____

_____

39

THOUGHTS & INSIGHTS

Challenges + **solutions**: _____

_____

_____

_____

_____

_____

Discoveries + lessons learned: _____

_____

_____

_____

_____

_____

_____

What I would **change** or **do differently**: _____

_____

_____

_____

_____

_____

_____

What I **like about my project**: _____

_____

_____

_____

_____

_____

_____

Things to try in the future: _____

_____

_____

_____

_____

_____

FINISHED PROJECT INFO

Suggested or **included** wearing/pairing items: _____

_____

_____

_____

_____

_____

_____

Kept, **gifted**, or **offered for sale**? _____

Price or **other valuation**: _____

If gifted or sold, **recipient**/**buyer** details: _____

_____

_____

_____

_____

_____

_____

_____

Other: _____

_____

_____

_____

_____

_____

_____

_____

_____

_____

FINISHED PROJECT PHOTO(S)

PROJECT 08

Type of Project/**Description**: _____

_____

Inspiration: _____

_____

Goals + **Intentions**: _____

_____

_____

_____

Style + **Color Scheme**: _____

Dimensions: _____

Date **Started**: _____ Date **Finished**: _____

Beads, **Gemstones** + **Other Products** Used: _____

_____

_____

_____

_____

Wire, Findings, Chain + **Other Hardware**: _____

_____

_____

_____

_____

Techniques + Methods: _____

_____

_____

_____

_____

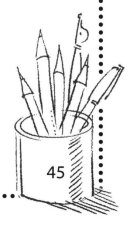

45

46

THOUGHTS & INSIGHTS

Challenges + **solutions**: _____

_____

_____

_____

_____

_____

Discoveries + lessons learned: _____

_____

_____

_____

_____

_____

What I would **change** or **do differently**: _____

_____

_____

_____

_____

_____

What I **like about my project**: _____

_____

_____

_____

_____

_____

Things to try in the future: _____

_____

_____

_____

_____

_____

FINISHED PROJECT INFO

Suggested or **included** wearing/pairing items: _____

_____

_____

_____

_____

_____

_____

Kept, **gifted**, or **offered for sale**? _____

Price or **other valuation**: _____

If gifted or sold, **recipient**/**buyer** details: _____

_____

_____

_____

_____

_____

_____

_____

Other: _____

_____

_____

_____

_____

_____

_____

_____

_____

_____

_____

FINISHED PROJECT PHOTO(S)

PROJECT 09

Type of Project/**Description:** _____

_____

Inspiration: _____

_____

Goals + **Intentions:** _____

_____

_____

_____

Style + **Color Scheme:** _____

Dimensions: _____

Date **Started:** _____   Date **Finished:** _____

Beads, Gemstones + **Other Products** Used: _____

_____

_____

_____

_____

Wire, Findings, Chain + **Other Hardware:** _____

_____

_____

_____

_____

Techniques + Methods: _____

_____

_____

_____

_____

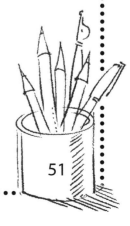

51

THOUGHTS & INSIGHTS

Challenges + **solutions**: _____

_____

_____

_____

_____

_____

Discoveries + lessons learned: _____

_____

_____

_____

_____

_____

What I would **change** or **do differently**: _____

_____

_____

_____

_____

_____

What I **like about my project**: _____

_____

_____

_____

_____

_____

Things to try in the future: _____

_____

_____

_____

_____

_____

FINISHED PROJECT INFO

Suggested or **included** wearing/pairing items: _____

_____

_____

_____

_____

_____

_____

Kept, **gifted**, or **offered for sale**? _____

Price or **other valuation**: _____

If gifted or sold, **recipient/buyer** details: _____

_____

_____

_____

_____

_____

_____

_____

Other: _____

_____

_____

_____

_____

_____

_____

_____

_____

_____

_____

FINISHED PROJECT PHOTO(S)

PROJECT 10

Type of Project/**Description**: _____

_____

Inspiration: _____

_____

Goals + **Intentions**: _____

_____

_____

_____

Style + **Color Scheme**: _____

Dimensions: _____

Date **Started**: _____ Date **Finished**: _____

Beads, **Gemstones** + **Other Products** Used: _____

_____

_____

_____

_____

Wire, Findings, Chain + **Other Hardware**: _____

_____

_____

_____

_____

Techniques + Methods: _____

_____

_____

_____

_____

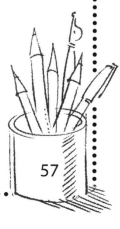

57

THOUGHTS & INSIGHTS

Challenges + **solutions**: _____

_____

_____

_____

_____

_____

Discoveries + lessons learned: _____

_____

_____

_____

_____

_____

_____

What I would **change** or **do differently**: _____

_____

_____

_____

_____

_____

What I **like about my project**: _____

_____

_____

_____

_____

_____

Things to try in the future: _____

_____

_____

_____

_____

_____

FINISHED PROJECT INFO

Suggested or **included** wearing/pairing items: _____

_____

_____

_____

_____

_____

_____

Kept, **gifted**, or **offered for sale**? _____

Price or **other valuation**: _____

If gifted or sold, **recipient/buyer** details: _____

_____

_____

_____

_____

_____

_____

_____

Other: _____

_____

_____

_____

_____

_____

_____

_____

_____

_____

_____

FINISHED PROJECT PHOTO(S)

PROJECT 11

Type of Project/**Description:** _____

_____

Inspiration: _____

_____

Goals + **Intentions:** _____

_____

_____

_____

Style + **Color Scheme:** _____

Dimensions: _____

Date **Started:** _____ Date **Finished:** _____

Beads, Gemstones + **Other Products** Used: _____

_____

_____

_____

_____

Wire, Findings, Chain + **Other Hardware:** _____

_____

_____

_____

_____

Techniques + Methods: _____

_____

_____

_____

_____

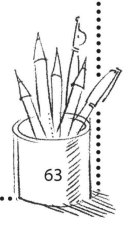

63

THOUGHTS & INSIGHTS

Challenges + **solutions**: _____

_____

_____

_____

_____

_____

Discoveries + lessons learned: _____

_____

_____

_____

_____

_____

What I would **change** or **do differently**: _____

_____

_____

_____

_____

_____

What I **like about my project**: _____

_____

_____

_____

_____

_____

Things to try in the future: _____

_____

_____

_____

_____

_____

FINISHED PROJECT INFO

Suggested or **included** wearing/pairing items: _____

_____

_____

_____

_____

_____

_____

Kept, **gifted**, or **offered for sale**? _____

Price or **other valuation**: _____

If gifted or sold, **recipient/buyer** details: _____

_____

_____

_____

_____

_____

_____

_____

Other: _____

_____

_____

_____

_____

_____

_____

_____

_____

_____

_____

FINISHED PROJECT PHOTO(S)

PROJECT 12

Type of Project/**Description**: _____

_____

Inspiration: _____

_____

Goals + **Intentions**: _____

_____

_____

_____

Style + **Color Scheme**: _____

Dimensions: _____

Date **Started**: _____ Date **Finished**: _____

Beads, Gemstones + **Other Products** Used: _____

_____

_____

_____

_____

Wire, Findings, Chain + **Other Hardware**: _____

_____

_____

_____

_____

Techniques + Methods: _____

_____

_____

_____

_____

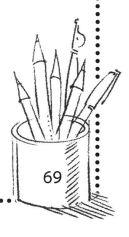

69

THOUGHTS & INSIGHTS

Challenges + **solutions**: _____

_____

_____

_____

_____

_____

Discoveries + lessons learned: _____

_____

_____

_____

_____

_____

What I would **change** or **do differently**: _____

_____

_____

_____

_____

_____

What I **like about my project**: _____

_____

_____

_____

_____

_____

Things to try in the future: _____

_____

_____

_____

_____

_____

FINISHED PROJECT INFO

Suggested or **included** wearing/pairing items: _____

_____

_____

_____

_____

_____

_____

Kept, **gifted**, or **offered for sale**? _____

Price or **other valuation**: _____

If gifted or sold, **recipient/buyer** details: _____

_____

_____

_____

_____

_____

_____

_____

Other: _____

_____

_____

_____

_____

_____

_____

_____

_____

_____

FINISHED PROJECT PHOTO(S)

PROJECT 13

Type of Project/**Description**: _____

_____

Inspiration: _____

_____

Goals + **Intentions**: _____

_____

_____

_____

Style + **Color Scheme**: _____

Dimensions: _____

Date **Started**: _____ Date **Finished**: _____

Beads, **Gemstones** + **Other Products** Used: _____

_____

_____

_____

_____

Wire, Findings, Chain + **Other Hardware**: _____

_____

_____

_____

_____

Techniques + Methods: _____

_____

_____

_____

_____

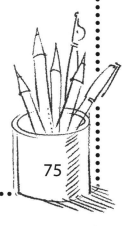

75

THOUGHTS & INSIGHTS

Challenges + **solutions**: _____

_____

_____

_____

_____

_____

Discoveries + lessons learned: _____

_____

_____

_____

_____

_____

What I would **change** or **do differently**: _____

_____

_____

_____

_____

_____

What I **like about my project**: _____

_____

_____

_____

_____

_____

Things to try in the future: _____

_____

_____

_____

_____

_____

FINISHED PROJECT INFO

Suggested or **included** wearing/pairing items: _____

_____

_____

_____

_____

_____

_____

Kept, **gifted**, or **offered for sale**? _____

Price or **other valuation**: _____

If gifted or sold, **recipient/buyer** details: _____

_____

_____

_____

_____

_____

_____

_____

Other: _____

_____

_____

_____

_____

_____

_____

_____

_____

_____

_____

FINISHED PROJECT PHOTO(S)

PROJECT 14

Type of Project/**Description**: _____

_____

Inspiration: _____

_____

Goals + **Intentions**: _____

_____

_____

_____

Style + **Color Scheme**: _____

Dimensions: _____

Date **Started**: _____   Date **Finished**: _____

Beads, Gemstones + **Other Products** Used: _____

_____

_____

_____

_____

Wire, Findings, Chain + **Other Hardware**: _____

_____

_____

_____

_____

Techniques + Methods: _____

_____

_____

_____

_____

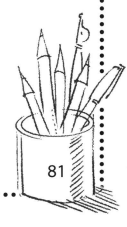

81

THOUGHTS & INSIGHTS

Challenges + **solutions**: _____

_____

_____

_____

_____

_____

Discoveries + lessons learned: _____

_____

_____

_____

_____

_____

What I would **change** or **do differently**: _____

_____

_____

_____

_____

_____

What I **like about my project**: _____

_____

_____

_____

_____

_____

Things to try in the future: _____

_____

_____

_____

_____

_____

FINISHED PROJECT INFO

Suggested or **included** wearing/pairing items: _____

_____

_____

_____

_____

_____

_____

Kept, **gifted**, or **offered for sale**? _____

Price or **other valuation**: _____

If gifted or sold, **recipient/buyer** details: _____

_____

_____

_____

_____

_____

_____

_____

Other: _____

_____

_____

_____

_____

_____

_____

_____

_____

_____

_____

_____

FINISHED PROJECT PHOTO(S)

PROJECT 15

Type of Project/**Description**: _____

_____

Inspiration: _____

_____

Goals + **Intentions**: _____

_____

_____

_____

Style + Color Scheme: _____

Dimensions: _____

Date **Started**: _____ Date **Finished**: _____

Beads, Gemstones + Other Products Used: _____

_____

_____

_____

_____

Wire, Findings, Chain + Other Hardware: _____

_____

_____

_____

_____

Techniques + Methods: _____

_____

_____

_____

_____

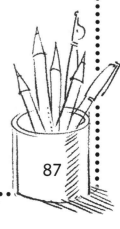

87

THOUGHTS & INSIGHTS

Challenges + **solutions**: _____

_____

_____

_____

_____

_____

Discoveries + lessons learned: _____

_____

_____

_____

_____

_____

What I would **change** or **do differently**: _____

_____

_____

_____

_____

_____

What I **like about my project**: _____

_____

_____

_____

_____

_____

Things to try in the future: _____

_____

_____

_____

_____

_____

FINISHED PROJECT INFO

Suggested or **included** wearing/pairing items: _____

_____

_____

_____

_____

_____

_____

Kept, **gifted**, or **offered for sale**? _____

Price or **other valuation**: _____

If gifted or sold, **recipient/buyer** details: _____

_____

_____

_____

_____

_____

_____

_____

_____

Other: _____

_____

_____

_____

_____

_____

_____

_____

_____

_____

_____

_____

FINISHED PROJECT PHOTO(S)

PROJECT 16

Type of Project/**Description**: _____

_____

Inspiration: _____

_____

Goals + **Intentions**: _____

_____

_____

_____

Style + **Color Scheme**: _____

Dimensions: _____

Date **Started**: _____ Date **Finished**: _____

Beads, **Gemstones** + **Other Products** Used: _____

_____

_____

_____

_____

Wire, Findings, Chain + **Other Hardware**: _____

_____

_____

_____

_____

Techniques + Methods: _____

_____

_____

_____

_____

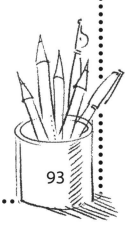

93

PROJECT SKETCH / PATTERN

THOUGHTS & INSIGHTS

Challenges + **solutions**: _____

_____

_____

_____

_____

_____

Discoveries + lessons learned: _____

_____

_____

_____

_____

_____

What I would **change** or **do differently**: _____

_____

_____

_____

_____

_____

What I **like about my project**: _____

_____

_____

_____

_____

_____

Things to try in the future: _____

_____

_____

_____

_____

_____

FINISHED PROJECT INFO

Suggested or **included** wearing/pairing items: _____

_____

_____

_____

_____

_____

_____

Kept, **gifted**, or **offered for sale**? _____

Price or **other valuation**: _____

If gifted or sold, **recipient/buyer** details: _____

_____

_____

_____

_____

_____

_____

_____

Other: _____

_____

_____

_____

_____

_____

_____

_____

_____

_____

_____

_____

FINISHED PROJECT PHOTO(S)

PROJECT 17

Type of Project/**Description**: _____

_____

Inspiration: _____

_____

Goals + **Intentions**: _____

_____

_____

_____

Style + **Color Scheme**: _____

Dimensions: _____

Date **Started**: _____ Date **Finished**: _____

Beads, Gemstones + **Other Products** Used: _____

_____

_____

_____

_____

Wire, Findings, Chain + **Other Hardware**: _____

_____

_____

_____

_____

Techniques + Methods: _____

_____

_____

_____

_____

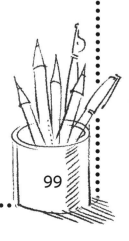

99

THOUGHTS & INSIGHTS

Challenges + **solutions**: _____

_____

_____

_____

_____

_____

Discoveries + lessons learned: _____

_____

_____

_____

_____

_____

What I would **change** or **do differently**: _____

_____

_____

_____

_____

_____

What I **like about my project**: _____

_____

_____

_____

_____

_____

Things to try in the future: _____

_____

_____

_____

_____

_____

FINISHED PROJECT INFO

Suggested or **included** wearing/pairing items: _____

_____

_____

_____

_____

_____

_____

Kept, **gifted**, or **offered for sale**? _____

Price or **other valuation**: _____

If gifted or sold, **recipient/buyer** details: _____

_____

_____

_____

_____

_____

_____

_____

Other: _____

_____

_____

_____

_____

_____

_____

_____

_____

_____

_____

_____

FINISHED PROJECT PHOTO(S)

PROJECT 18

Type of Project/**Description:** _____

_____

Inspiration: _____

_____

Goals + **Intentions:** _____

_____

_____

_____

Style + **Color Scheme:** _____

Dimensions: _____

Date **Started:** _____ Date **Finished:** _____

Beads, Gemstones + Other Products Used: _____

_____

_____

_____

_____

Wire, Findings, Chain + Other Hardware: _____

_____

_____

_____

_____

Techniques + Methods: _____

_____

_____

_____

_____

REFERENCE PHOTO(S) / INSTRUCTIONS

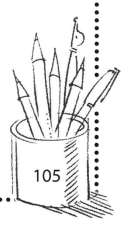

105

THOUGHTS & INSIGHTS

Challenges + **solutions**: _____

_____

_____

_____

_____

_____

Discoveries + lessons learned: _____

_____

_____

_____

_____

_____

What I would **change** or **do differently**: _____

_____

_____

_____

_____

_____

What I **like about my project**: _____

_____

_____

_____

_____

_____

Things to try in the future: _____

_____

_____

_____

_____

_____

FINISHED PROJECT INFO

Suggested or **included** wearing/pairing items: _____

_____

_____

_____

_____

_____

_____

Kept, **gifted**, or **offered for sale**? _____

Price or **other valuation**: _____

If gifted or sold, **recipient/buyer** details: _____

_____

_____

_____

_____

_____

_____

_____

Other: _____

_____

_____

_____

_____

_____

_____

_____

_____

_____

_____

FINISHED PROJECT PHOTO(S)

PROJECT 19

Type of Project/**Description**: _____

_____

Inspiration: _____

_____

Goals + **Intentions**: _____

_____

_____

_____

Style + **Color Scheme**: _____

Dimensions: _____

Date **Started**: _____   Date **Finished**: _____

Beads, **Gemstones** + **Other Products** Used: _____

_____

_____

_____

_____

Wire, Findings, Chain + **Other Hardware**: _____

_____

_____

_____

_____

Techniques + Methods: _____

_____

_____

_____

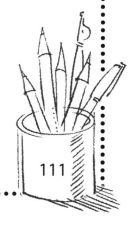

111

PROJECT SKETCH / PATTERN

THOUGHTS & INSIGHTS

Challenges + **solutions**: _____

_____

_____

_____

_____

_____

Discoveries + lessons learned: _____

_____

_____

_____

_____

_____

What I would **change** or **do differently**: _____

_____

_____

_____

_____

_____

What I **like about my project**: _____

_____

_____

_____

_____

_____

Things to try in the future: _____

_____

_____

_____

_____

_____

FINISHED PROJECT INFO

Suggested or **included** wearing/pairing items: _____

_____

_____

_____

_____

_____

_____

Kept, **gifted**, or **offered for sale**? _____

Price or **other valuation**: _____

If gifted or sold, **recipient/buyer** details: _____

_____

_____

_____

_____

_____

_____

_____

Other: _____

_____

_____

_____

_____

_____

_____

_____

_____

_____

_____

FINISHED PROJECT PHOTO(S)

PROJECT 20

Type of Project/**Description**: _____

_____

Inspiration: _____

_____

Goals + **Intentions**: _____

_____

_____

_____

Style + **Color Scheme**: _____

Dimensions: _____

Date **Started**: _____ Date **Finished**: _____

Beads, **Gemstones** + **Other Products** Used: _____

_____

_____

_____

_____

Wire, Findings, Chain + Other Hardware: _____

_____

_____

_____

_____

Techniques + Methods: _____

_____

_____

_____

_____

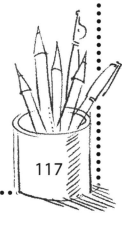

117

118

THOUGHTS & INSIGHTS

Challenges + **solutions**: _____

_____

_____

_____

_____

_____

Discoveries + lessons learned: _____

_____

_____

_____

_____

_____

What I would **change** or **do differently**: _____

_____

_____

_____

_____

_____

What I **like about my project**: _____

_____

_____

_____

_____

_____

Things to try in the future: _____

_____

_____

_____

_____

_____

FINISHED PROJECT INFO

Suggested or **included** wearing/pairing items: _____

_____

_____

_____

_____

_____

_____

Kept, **gifted**, or **offered for sale**? _____

Price or **other valuation**: _____

If gifted or sold, **recipient/buyer** details: _____

_____

_____

_____

_____

_____

_____

_____

Other: _____

_____

_____

_____

_____

_____

_____

_____

_____

_____

_____

_____

FINISHED PROJECT PHOTO(S)

PROJECT 21

Type of Project/**Description**: _____

_____

Inspiration: _____

_____

Goals + **Intentions**: _____

_____

_____

_____

Style + **Color Scheme**: _____

Dimensions: _____

Date **Started**: _____ Date **Finished**: _____

Beads, **Gemstones** + **Other Products** Used: _____

_____

_____

_____

_____

Wire, Findings, Chain + **Other Hardware**: _____

_____

_____

_____

_____

Techniques + Methods: _____

_____

_____

_____

_____

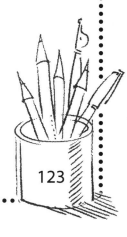

123

PROJECT SKETCH / PATTERN

THOUGHTS & INSIGHTS

Challenges + **solutions**: _____

_____

_____

_____

_____

_____

Discoveries + lessons learned: _____

_____

_____

_____

_____

_____

What I would **change** or **do differently**: _____

_____

_____

_____

_____

_____

What I **like about my project**: _____

_____

_____

_____

_____

_____

Things to try in the future: _____

_____

_____

_____

_____

_____

FINISHED PROJECT INFO

Suggested or **included** wearing/pairing items: _____

_____

_____

_____

_____

_____

_____

Kept, **gifted**, or **offered for sale**? _____

Price or **other valuation**: _____

If gifted or sold, **recipient/buyer** details: _____

_____

_____

_____

_____

_____

_____

_____

Other: _____

_____

_____

_____

_____

_____

_____

_____

_____

_____

_____

FINISHED PROJECT PHOTO(S)

PROJECT 22

Type of Project/**Description**: _____

_____

Inspiration: _____

_____

Goals + **Intentions**: _____

_____

_____

_____

Style + **Color Scheme**: _____

Dimensions: _____

Date **Started**: _____ Date **Finished**: _____

Beads, **Gemstones** + **Other Products** Used: _____

_____

_____

_____

_____

Wire, **Findings**, **Chain** + **Other Hardware**: _____

_____

_____

_____

_____

Techniques + Methods: _____

_____

_____

_____

_____

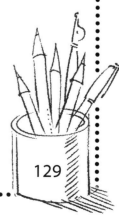

129

PROJECT SKETCH / PATTERN

THOUGHTS & INSIGHTS

Challenges + **solutions**: _____

_____

_____

_____

_____

_____

Discoveries + lessons learned: _____

_____

_____

_____

_____

_____

What I would **change** or **do differently**: _____

_____

_____

_____

_____

_____

What I **like about my project**: _____

_____

_____

_____

_____

_____

Things to try in the future: _____

_____

_____

_____

_____

_____

FINISHED PROJECT INFO

Suggested or **included** wearing/pairing items: _____

_____

_____

_____

_____

_____

_____

Kept, **gifted**, or **offered for sale**? _____

Price or **other valuation**: _____

If gifted or sold, **recipient/buyer** details: _____

_____

_____

_____

_____

_____

_____

_____

Other: _____

_____

_____

_____

_____

_____

_____

_____

_____

_____

_____

FINISHED PROJECT PHOTO(S)

PROJECT 23

Type of Project/**Description:** _____

_____

Inspiration: _____

_____

Goals + **Intentions:** _____

_____

_____

_____

Style + Color Scheme: _____

Dimensions: _____

Date **Started:** _____   Date **Finished:** _____

Beads, Gemstones + Other Products Used: _____

_____

_____

_____

_____

Wire, Findings, Chain + Other Hardware: _____

_____

_____

_____

_____

Techniques + Methods: _____

_____

_____

_____

_____

135

PROJECT SKETCH / PATTERN

THOUGHTS & INSIGHTS

Challenges + **solutions**: _____

_____

_____

_____

_____

_____

Discoveries + lessons learned: _____

_____

_____

_____

_____

_____

What I would **change** or **do differently**: _____

_____

_____

_____

_____

_____

What I **like about my project**: _____

_____

_____

_____

_____

_____

Things to try in the future: _____

_____

_____

_____

_____

_____

FINISHED PROJECT INFO

Suggested or **included** wearing/pairing items: _____

_____

_____

_____

_____

_____

_____

Kept, **gifted**, or **offered for sale**? _____

Price or **other valuation**: _____

If gifted or sold, **recipient/buyer** details: _____

_____

_____

_____

_____

_____

_____

_____

_____

Other: _____

_____

_____

_____

_____

_____

_____

_____

_____

_____

_____

FINISHED PROJECT PHOTO(S)

PROJECT 24

Type of Project/**Description**: _____

_____

Inspiration: _____

_____

Goals + **Intentions**: _____

_____

_____

_____

Style + **Color Scheme**: _____

Dimensions: _____

Date **Started**: _____ Date **Finished**: _____

Beads, Gemstones + **Other Products** Used: _____

_____

_____

_____

_____

Wire, Findings, Chain + **Other Hardware**: _____

_____

_____

_____

_____

Techniques + Methods: _____

_____

_____

_____

_____

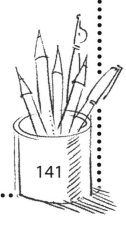

141

THOUGHTS & INSIGHTS

Challenges + **solutions**: _____

_____

_____

_____

_____

_____

Discoveries + lessons learned: _____

_____

_____

_____

_____

_____

What I would **change** or **do differently**: _____

_____

_____

_____

_____

_____

What I **like about my project**: _____

_____

_____

_____

_____

_____

Things to try in the future: _____

_____

_____

_____

_____

_____

FINISHED PROJECT INFO

Suggested or **included** wearing/pairing items: _____

_____

_____

_____

_____

_____

Kept, **gifted**, or **offered for sale**? _____

Price or **other valuation**: _____

If gifted or sold, **recipient/buyer** details: _____

_____

_____

_____

_____

_____

_____

_____

Other: _____

_____

_____

_____

_____

_____

_____

_____

_____

_____

_____

FINISHED PROJECT PHOTO(S)

PROJECT 25

Type of Project/**Description**: _____

_____

Inspiration: _____

_____

Goals + **Intentions**: _____

_____

_____

_____

Style + **Color Scheme**: _____

Dimensions: _____

Date **Started**: _____ Date **Finished**: _____

Beads, **Gemstones** + **Other Products** Used: _____

_____

_____

_____

_____

Wire, Findings, Chain + **Other Hardware**: _____

_____

_____

_____

_____

Techniques + Methods: _____

_____

_____

_____

_____

147

THOUGHTS & INSIGHTS

Challenges + **solutions**: _____

_____

_____

_____

_____

_____

Discoveries + lessons learned: _____

_____

_____

_____

_____

_____

What I would **change** or **do differently**: _____

_____

_____

_____

_____

_____

What I **like about my project**: _____

_____

_____

_____

_____

_____

Things to try in the future: _____

_____

_____

_____

_____

FINISHED PROJECT INFO

Suggested or **included** wearing/pairing items: _____

_____

_____

_____

_____

_____

_____

Kept, **gifted**, or **offered for sale**? _____

Price or **other valuation**: _____

If gifted or sold, **recipient/buyer** details: _____

_____

_____

_____

_____

_____

_____

_____

Other: _____

_____

_____

_____

_____

_____

_____

_____

_____

_____

_____

_____

FINISHED PROJECT PHOTO(S)

PROJECT 26

Type of Project/**Description**: _____

_____

Inspiration: _____

_____

Goals + **Intentions**: _____

_____

_____

_____

Style + **Color Scheme**: _____

Dimensions: _____

Date **Started**: _____ Date **Finished**: _____

Beads, **Gemstones** + **Other Products** Used: _____

_____

_____

_____

_____

Wire, Findings, Chain + **Other Hardware**: _____

_____

_____

_____

_____

Techniques + Methods: _____

_____

_____

_____

_____

REFERENCE PHOTO(S) / INSTRUCTIONS

153

PROJECT SKETCH / PATTERN

THOUGHTS & INSIGHTS

Challenges + **solutions**: _____
_____
_____
_____
_____
_____

Discoveries + lessons learned: _____
_____
_____
_____
_____
_____

What I would **change** or **do differently**: _____
_____
_____
_____
_____
_____

What I **like about my project**: _____
_____
_____
_____
_____
_____

Things to try in the future: _____
_____
_____
_____
_____
_____

FINISHED PROJECT INFO

Suggested or **included** wearing/pairing items: _____

_____

_____

_____

_____

_____

_____

Kept, **gifted**, or **offered for sale**? _____

Price or **other valuation**: _____

If gifted or sold, **recipient/buyer** details: _____

_____

_____

_____

_____

_____

_____

_____

Other: _____

_____

_____

_____

_____

_____

_____

_____

_____

_____

FINISHED PROJECT PHOTO(S)

PROJECT 27

Type of Project/**Description:** _____

_____

Inspiration: _____

_____

Goals + **Intentions:** _____

_____

_____

_____

Style + Color Scheme: _____

Dimensions: _____

Date **Started:** _____ Date **Finished:** _____

Beads, Gemstones + Other Products Used: _____

_____

_____

_____

_____

Wire, Findings, Chain + Other Hardware: _____

_____

_____

_____

_____

Techniques + Methods: _____

_____

_____

_____

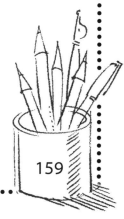

159

PROJECT SKETCH / PATTERN

THOUGHTS & INSIGHTS

Challenges + **solutions**: _____

_____

_____

_____

_____

_____

Discoveries + lessons learned: _____

_____

_____

_____

_____

_____

What I would **change** or **do differently**: _____

_____

_____

_____

_____

_____

What I **like about my project**: _____

_____

_____

_____

_____

_____

Things to try in the future: _____

_____

_____

_____

_____

_____

FINISHED PROJECT INFO

Suggested or **included** wearing/pairing items: _____

_____

_____

_____

_____

_____

_____

Kept, **gifted**, or **offered for sale**? _____

Price or **other valuation**: _____

If gifted or sold, **recipient/buyer** details: _____

_____

_____

_____

_____

_____

_____

_____

Other: _____

_____

_____

_____

_____

_____

_____

_____

_____

_____

_____

_____

FINISHED PROJECT PHOTO(S)

PROJECT 28

Type of Project/**Description**: _____

_____

Inspiration: _____

_____

Goals + **Intentions**: _____

_____

_____

_____

Style + **Color Scheme**: _____

Dimensions: _____

Date **Started**: _____ Date **Finished**: _____

Beads, Gemstones + **Other Products** Used: _____

_____

_____

_____

_____

Wire, Findings, Chain + **Other Hardware**: _____

_____

_____

_____

_____

Techniques + Methods: _____

_____

_____

_____

_____

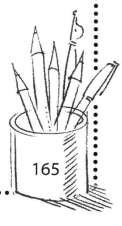

165

THOUGHTS & INSIGHTS

Challenges + **solutions**: _____
_____
_____
_____
_____
_____

Discoveries + lessons learned: _____
_____
_____
_____
_____
_____

What I would **change** or **do differently**: _____
_____
_____
_____
_____
_____

What I **like about my project**: _____
_____
_____
_____
_____
_____

Things to try in the future: _____
_____
_____
_____
_____
_____

FINISHED PROJECT INFO

Suggested or **included** wearing/pairing items: _____

_____

_____

_____

_____

_____

_____

Kept, **gifted**, or **offered for sale**? _____

Price or **other valuation**: _____

If gifted or sold, **recipient/buyer** details: _____

_____

_____

_____

_____

_____

_____

Other: _____

_____

_____

_____

_____

_____

_____

_____

_____

_____

_____

FINISHED PROJECT PHOTO(S)

PROJECT 29

Type of Project/**Description**: _____

_____

Inspiration: _____

_____

Goals + **Intentions**: _____

_____

_____

_____

Style + **Color Scheme**: _____

Dimensions: _____

Date **Started**: _____ Date **Finished**: _____

Beads, **Gemstones** + **Other Products** Used: _____

_____

_____

_____

_____

Wire, Findings, Chain + **Other Hardware**: _____

_____

_____

_____

_____

Techniques + Methods: _____

_____

_____

_____

_____

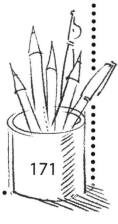

171

172

THOUGHTS & INSIGHTS

Challenges + **solutions**: _____

_____

_____

_____

_____

_____

Discoveries + lessons learned: _____

_____

_____

_____

_____

_____

What I would **change** or **do differently**: _____

_____

_____

_____

_____

_____

What I **like about my project**: _____

_____

_____

_____

_____

_____

Things to try in the future: _____

_____

_____

_____

_____

_____

FINISHED PROJECT INFO

Suggested or **included** wearing/pairing items: _____

_____

_____

_____

_____

_____

_____

Kept, **gifted**, or **offered for sale**? _____

Price or **other valuation**: _____

If gifted or sold, **recipient/buyer** details: _____

_____

_____

_____

_____

_____

_____

_____

Other: _____

_____

_____

_____

_____

_____

_____

_____

_____

_____

_____

FINISHED PROJECT PHOTO(S)

PROJECT 30

Type of Project/**Description**: _____

_____

Inspiration: _____

_____

Goals + **Intentions**: _____

_____

_____

_____

Style + **Color Scheme**: _____

Dimensions: _____

Date **Started**: _____ Date **Finished**: _____

Beads, Gemstones + **Other Products** Used: _____

_____

_____

_____

_____

Wire, Findings, Chain + **Other Hardware**: _____

_____

_____

_____

_____

Techniques + Methods: _____

_____

_____

_____

_____

177

PROJECT SKETCH / PATTERN

THOUGHTS & INSIGHTS

Challenges + **solutions**: _____

_____

_____

_____

_____

_____

Discoveries + lessons learned: _____

_____

_____

_____

_____

_____

What I would **change** or **do differently**: _____

_____

_____

_____

_____

_____

What I **like about my project**: _____

_____

_____

_____

_____

_____

Things to try in the future: _____

_____

_____

_____

_____

_____

FINISHED PROJECT INFO

Suggested or **included** wearing/pairing items: _____

_____

_____

_____

_____

_____

_____

Kept, **gifted**, or **offered for sale**? _____

Price or **other valuation**: _____

If gifted or sold, **recipient/buyer** details: _____

_____

_____

_____

_____

_____

_____

_____

Other: _____

_____

_____

_____

_____

_____

_____

_____

_____

_____

_____

FINISHED PROJECT PHOTO(S)

NOTES

NOTES

ABOUT THE AUTHOR

WHO IS RENA TUCKER?

Avid journal writer, artist, author, publisher, and founder of the groundbreaking Journal a Month Club, Rena loves *all* things creative.

Decades of navigating the myriad ups, downs, joys, pains, challenges and rewards of living the creative life have led her to conclude that "self-expression is not for sissies."

Known for her contagious enthusiasm and irreverent sense of humor, Rena is passionate about helping people be more empowered and enjoy greater freedom, happiness, and well-being. She's also passionate about naps, chardonnay, and the color periwinkle.

PERSONAL TRIVIA

- Won the Maury Brennan Ford pumpkin carving contest in 6th grade
- Earned a bachelor's degree in Business and a minor degree in English
- Was invited to be a professional ballroom dance instructor
- Trained in Taekwondo, Aikido, boxing, kickboxing, knives, and all manner of firearms
- Trained in classic portraiture with some of the most renowned artists of our time
- Obsessed with mosaics to the point she now dreams about grout lines and tesserae
- Dedicated "colorist" (fancy term for person who colors in adult coloring books)
- Is owned by Robbie the Black-Headed Caique, a feisty 5-ounce branch-hopping parrot
- Married her best friend, Jeff Tucker, on New Year's Eve 1996
- Plays the Celtic lap harp, but sadly, not very well

CONNECT WITH RENA

Check out Rena's books at www.Amazon.Com/author/renatucker and her website/blog that's chock-full of resources, inspiration, humor, and all manner of journaling goodness: www.JournalsRock.com.

The Ultimate SKETCH JOURNAL Series

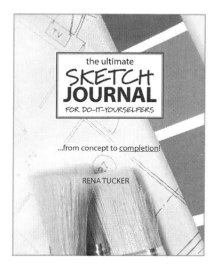

DO-IT-YOURSELFERS

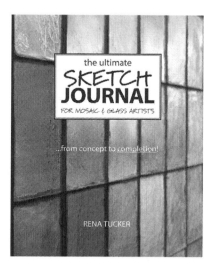

MOSAIC & GLASS ARTISTS

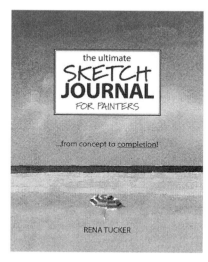

PAINTERS

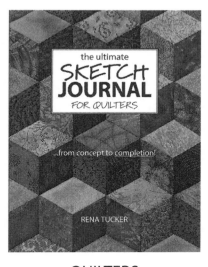

QUILTERS

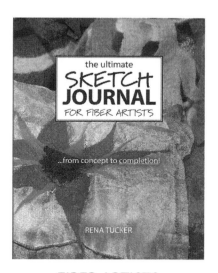

FIBER ARTISTS

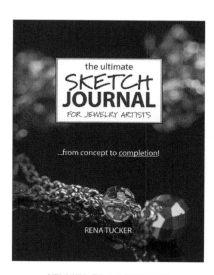

JEWELRY ARTISTS

...COLLECT THEM ALL!

FREE GOODIES FOR YOU

SCAN THE CODE FOR THE LATEST JOURNALING AWESOMENESS...

SIGN UP FOR WEEKLY JOURNAL PROMPTS + NEWS AND RECEIVE INSTANT ACCESS TO A DOWNLOADABLE MINI JOURNAL!

IDEAS • INSPIRATION • CREATIVITY • COMMUNITY

WWW.JOURNALSROCK.COM

Printed in Poland
by Amazon Fulfillment
Poland Sp. z o.o., Wrocław